Michael Jacques

Sounds Good!

for Violin

The Associated Board of
the Royal Schools of Music

SOUNDS GOOD!

1
Hoe-down

MICHAEL JACQUES

AB 2377

2
Starlight Serenade

3
Tropical Tango

Michael Jacques

Sounds Good!

for Violin

The Associated Board of
the Royal Schools of Music

SOUNDS GOOD!
1
Hoe-down

VIOLIN

MICHAEL JACQUES

AB 2377

2
Starlight Serenade

3
Tropical Tango

4
Promenade

5
Fiesta

AB 2377

4
Promenade

Warm and expressive ($\quad = 72$)

5
Fiesta

Carefree and rhythmic ($\text{♩.} = 88$)

Printed in England by Caligraving Limited Thetford Norfolk

AB 2377

3:94